G-2433-P

$1.50

MUSIC FROM TAIZÉ

By Jacques Berthier

PEOPLE'S EDITION

Also available:

MUSIC FROM TAIZÉ — Vocal Edition
G-2433

MUSIC FROM TAIZÉ — Instrumental Edition
G-2433-A

TAIZÉ—CANTATE! — Stereo recording made
at Taizé — MS-156 (Record or Cassette)

TAIZÉ IN ROME — Stereo recording made
during the 1981 pilgrimage to Rome
MS-157 (Record or Cassette)

Published by

G.I.A. Publications, Inc.
7404 So. Mason Avenue
Chicago, Illinois 60638

FOREWORD

Hidden away in the hills of Burgundy, in the eastern part of France, is an ecumenical community of brothers whose prayer is at the heart of their life. Founded in 1940, this community made up of Protestants and Catholics, from some 20 different countries, has become host to thousands of young people who visit Taizé, entering into the prayer and spirit of the community.

With the growing number of young people from all over the world coming to Taizé, a form of song that could enable people with no common langauge to participate in the community's prayer had to be developed. With the help of Jacques Berthier, musician and friend of Taizé, different methods were tested, and a solution found in the use of repetitive structures—short musical phrases with singable easily memorized melodies—and some very basic Latin texts. To this was added verses for cantor in numerous living languages. The experiment proved to be an overwhelming success, as one can easily verify by listening to either of the two recordings made during the actual prayer services—one at Taizé and one during the pilgrimage to Rome.

The present American edition of the MUSIC FROM TAIZÉ retains the beautiful Latin refrains, which because of the natural "color" of the language, bear up under constant repetition better than any vernacular. In this edition, however, all verses have been translated and adapted into English.

The people's melodies contained in this edition, are in the form of responses, litanies, acclamations and canons (rounds). Added to these are numerous choral harmonies, secondary refrains or canons, and a delightful array of instrumental solos and accompaniments for various instruments. This material is found in the Vocal and Instrumental Editions.

The Music of Taizé is performable by small groups with a simple guitar or keyboard accompaniment, or larger groups of hundreds or even thousands accompanied by choir, brass, strings, woodwinds, organ and percussion.

For a more thorough introduction to the music and its origin, see the foreword to the Vocal and Instrumental Editions.

TABLE OF CONTENTS

I. OSTINATO RESPONSES AND CHORALES (1)

II. LITANIES AND OTHER TEXTS WITH REFRAINS (40)

III. ACCLAMATIONS (72)

IV. CANONS (82)

BEATI 3

Happy they who dwell in God's house.

Principal Ostinato Response

Be - a - ti in do-mo Do-mi-ni Be -

Secondary Ostinato (Unison or Canon)

Be - a - ti Be - a - ti Be - a - ti Be -

a - ti Be - a - ti Be - a - ti Be -

BEATI PACIFICI 5

Blest are the peacemakers, and blest the pure in heart, for they shall see God.

Ostinato Chorale

Be - a - ti pa - ci - fi - ci Be - a - ti mun - do cor - de

quo-ni - am i - psi De-um i - psi De-um vi - de-bunt.

6   # CRUCEM TUAM

We adore your cross, O Lord, and we praise your resurrection.

Ostinato Chorale

Cru-cem tu - am a-do-ra-mus Do-mi - ne, re-sur - rec - ti - o -nem

tu-am lau -da-mus Do-mi - ne. Lau-da-mus et glo - ri - fi - ca - mus.

(Fine)

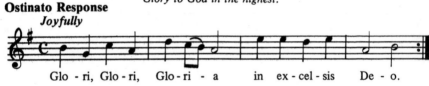

Re-sur-rec-ti - o -nem tu-am lau-da - mus Do-mi - ne. Cru - cem tu -

7   # GLORIA I

Glory to God in the highest.

Ostinato Response

Joyfully

Glo - ri, Glo - ri, Glo -ri - a in ex - cel - sis De - o.

8   # HOW BLESSED ARE YOU

Chorale *p*

How blessed are you who are poor; the

King-dom of God is yours, how blessed are you who are

(Fine)

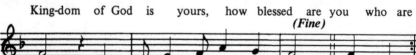

poor; the King - dom of God is yours. _____ How

JESUS, REMEMBER ME

Ostinato Response

Je - sus, re - mem - ber me

when you come in - to your King - dom. Je - sus, re -

mem - ber me when you come in - to your King - dom.

LAUDATE DOMINUM

Praise the Lord, all you peoples.

Chorale

Lau - da - te Do - mi - num, Lau-da - te Do-mi-num om - nes

1.

2.

D.C.

gen - tes, Al - le - lu - ia. Al - le - lu - ia.

LAUDATE OMNES GENTES

All peoples, praise the Lord.

Ostinato Chorale

p

Lau - da - te om - nes gen - tes, lau -

da - te Do - mi - num. Lau - da - te om - nes

(Fine)

gen - tes, lau - da - te Do - mi - num! Lau -

13   # MANDATUM NOVUM

I give you a new commandment, says the Lord: Love one another as I have loved you.

Theme (Ostinato Response or Canon)

Man - da - tum no - vum do___ vo - bis, di - cit Do - mi -

nus, di - cit Do - mi - nus._____

18   # MISERERE MEI

Turn to me, have mercy on me, for I am alone and poor.

Ostinato Response

Calmly

Mi - se - re - re me - i Do - mi - ne mi - se - re - re.

20   # MISERERE NOBIS

Ostinato Response   *Have mercy on us, O Lord.*

Mi - se - re - re no - bis Do - mi - ne, mi - se - re - re no - bis.

Mi - se - re - re no - bis Do - mi - ne, mi - se - re - re no - bis.

21   # MISERICORDIAS DOMINI

Ostinato *p*   *For ever will I sing the mercy of the Lord.*

Mi - se - ri - cor - di - as Do - mi - ni in ae - ter - num can - ta - bo.

Canticle of Simeon
NUNC DIMITTIS 22

Now, Lord, you can let your servant go in peace according to your promise.

Chorale

Lento

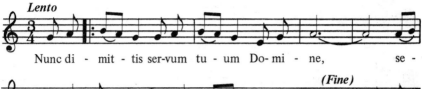

Nunc di - mit - tis ser-vum tu - um Do- mi - ne, se -

(Fine)

cun - dum ver-bum tu - um in pa - ce. Nunc di -

Lord's Prayer
PATER NOSTER 23

Ostinato Response

(Fine)

Pa - ter no - ster qui es in coe - lis Pa - ter

Magnificat II
SANCTUM NOMEN DOMINI 25

My soul magnifies the holy name of the Lord.

Ostinato Chorale

San - ctum no-men Do-mi - ni ma-gni - fi - cat __ a-ni - ma me - a.

San-ctum no-men Do-mi - ni ma-gni-fi-cat a-ni - ma me- a.

28

UBI CARITAS

Where charity and love are found, God himself is there.

Ostinato Response

U - bi ca - ri - tas et a - mor,

U - bi ca - ri - tas De - us i - bi est.

36

VENI SANCTE SPIRITUS

Come, Holy Spirit

Ostinato Response

Ve - ni San - cte Spi - ri - tus.____

42

ADORAMUS TE DOMINE I

We adore you, O Lord.

Refrain

A - do - ra - mus te, A - do - ra - mus te, Do - mi - ne.

44

ADORAMUS TE DOMINE II — GLORIA

We adore you, O Lord. — Glory to God in the highest.

A - do - ra - mus te Do - mi - ne.

Alternate Refrains

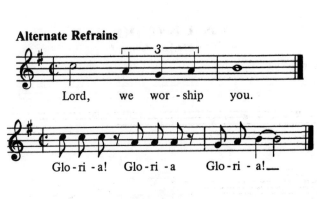

Lord, we wor - ship you.

Glo - ri - a! Glo - ri - a Glo - ri - a!__

CREDO I   47

We believe in one God, in one Lord, in one Spirit.

Refrain

Cre - do in u - num De - um, cre - do in u - num Do - mi - num.
Spi - ri - tum.

* 1st time: Dominum; 2nd time: Spiritum.

DOMINE MISERERE I-II   49

Lord, have mercy on us.

Domine Miserere 1 - Refrain

Do - mi - ne mi - se - re - re.

Domine Miserere 2 - Refrain

Do - mi - ne, Do - mi - ne mi - se - re - re.

EXAUDI NOS   50

Refrain   *Hear us*

Ex - au - di - nos; ex - au - di - nos.
Lord, hear our prayer, Lord, hear our prayer.

11

51

GLORIA TIBI DOMINE
Glory to you, O Lord.

Refrain

Glo - ri - a ti - bi Do - mi - ne.

Canon

Glo - ri - a ti - bi Do - mi - ne, Do - mi - ne,

Glo - ri - a ti - bi Do - mi - ne, Do - mi - ne.

53

JESU CHRISTE MISERERE
Jesus Christ have mercy on us.

Refrain

Je - su Chri - ste mi - se - re - re.

55

KYRIE ELEISON I-X
Lord, have mercy.

Kyrie 1

Ky - ri - e, Ky - ri - e, e - le - i - son.

Kyrie 2

Ky - ri - e, e - le - i - son.

Kyrie 3

Ky - ri - e e - le - i - son, E - le - i - son.

Kyrie 4

Ky - ri - e e - le - i - son, e - le - i - son.

Kyrie 5

Ky - ri - e e - le - i - son, e le - i - son.

Kyrie 6

Ky - ri - e e - le - i - son, Ky - ri - e e - le - i - son.

Kyrie 7

Ky - ri - e e - le - i - son, Ky - ri - e e - le - i - son.

Kyrie 8

Ky - ri - e e - le - i - son, Ky - ri - e e - le - i - son.

Kyrie 9

Ky-ri - e, Ky-ri - e, Ky-ri - e, e - le - i -

son.

Kyrie 10

Ky - ri - e, Ky - ri - e, e - le - i - son;

Ky - ri - e, Ky - ri - e, e - le - i - son.

60   # LIBERA NOS DOMINE
Deliver us, O Lord.

A Verse Cantor   **B** Refrain All

Li - be - ra - nos Do - mi - ne.

C Cantor   **D** All

Li - be - ra nos Do - mi - ne.

MARANATHA! ALLELUIA! I 62

Come soon! Alleluia!

Ma - ra -na - tha,   Ma - ra - na - tha!

Al - le - lu - ia,   al - le - lu - ia!

MEMENTO NOSTRI DOMINE 63

Remember us, O Lord.

Me - men - to no - stri Do - mi - ne.

Me - men - to no - stri Do - mi - ne.

Me - men - to no - stri Do - mi - ne.

Me - men - to no - stri Do - mi - ne.

Mo - men - to no - stri Do - mi - ne.

Me - men - to no - stri Do - mi - ne.

Me - men - to no-stri Do - mi - ne.   Me-men - to no - stri Do - mi - ne.

66   O CHRISTE AUDI NOS

O Christ, hear us.

Refrain

O   Chri - ste   au - di - nos.
Hear   us,   O   Christ, Our Lord.

66   TE ROGAMUS AUDI NOS

We ask you to hear us.

Refrain

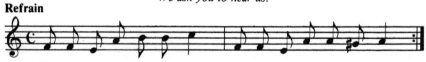

Te ro - ga - mus au - di   nos,   te ro - ga - mus au - di   nos,

VENI CREATOR SPIRITUS

Come, Creator Spirit

Ve - ni Cre - a - tor Spi - ri - tus.

VENI LUMEN CORDIUM I-II

Come, light of our hearts. Come, Holy Spirit.

Veni Lumen Cordium 1

Ve - ni lu - men cor - di - um.

Veni Lumen Cordium 2

Ve - ni lu - men cor - di - um.

ALLELUIAS I-VI

Alleluia 1

Al - le - lu - ia, al - le - lu - ia!

Al - le - lu - ia, al - le - lu - ia!

Alleluia 2

Al - le - lu - ia, al - le - lu - ia.

Alleluia 3

Al - le - lu - ia, ____ Al - le - lu - ia! ____

Alleluia 4

Al - le - lu - ia, al - le - lu - ia, al - le - lu - ia!

Alleluia 5

Al - le - lu - ia, al - le - lu - ia. Al - le -

lu - ia, al - le - lu - ia!

Alleluia 6

Al - le - lu - ia, Al - le - lu - ia,

Al - le - lu - ia! ia!

Amen 1

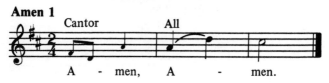

A - men, A - men.

Amen 2

A - men, A - men.

Amen 3

A - men, A - men, A - men,

A - men, Al - le - lu - ia. Al - le - lu - ia.
A - men, A - men.

HOSANNA FILIO DAVID 78
Hosanna to the Son of David.

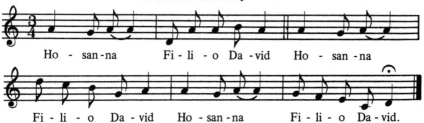

Ho - san - na Fi - li - o Da - vid Ho - san - na

Fi - li - o Da - vid Ho - san - na Fi - li - o Da - vid.

MARANATHA — ALLELUIA II 78
Come soon! Alleluia!

Ma - ra - na - tha, Al - le - lu - ia, al - le - lu - ia.

79

MARANATHA — VENI DOMINE

Come soon. Come, Lord, and do not delay.

Ma-ra-na-tha, ma-ra-na-tha, Ve-ni Do-mi-ne, No-li tar-da-re.

79

MYSTERIUM FIDEI

The mystery of faith. Savior of the world, save us. By your cross and your resurrection you have delivered us.

Mys-te-ri-um fi-de-i, mys-te-ri-um fi-de-i.

80

SANCTUS DOMINUS

Holy Lord

San-ctus, San-ctus, San-ctus Do-mi-nus.

80

TU SOLUS SANCTUS I-II

You alone are Holy, you alone are Lord, you alone, O Jesus Christ, are Most High.

Tu Solus Sanctus 1

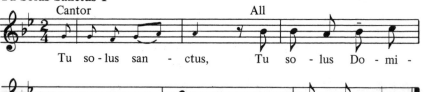

Tu so-lus san-ctus, Tu so-lus Do-mi-

nus, Tu so-lus al-tis-si-mus.

Tu Solus Sanctus 2

Tu so-lus san - ctus, Tu so-lus Do - mi - nus, Tu so-lus al -

tis - si - mus Je - su Chri - ste.

UNUM CORPUS 81
One Body and one Spirit.

U - num Cor - pus   et   u - nus Spi - ri - tus.

AGNUS DEI 85
Lamb of God, you take away the sins of the world, have mercy on us; grant us peace.

Canon

A - gnus De - i   qui   tol - lis   pec - ca - ta

mun - di,   Mi - se - re - re   no - bis.
(Do - na   no - bis   pa - cem.)

86 ALLELUIA

Canon

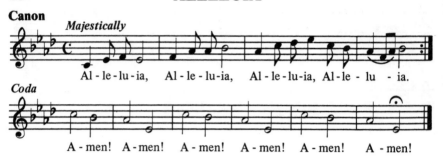

Majestically

Al - le - lu - ia, Al - le - lu - ia, Al - le - lu - ia, Al - le - lu - ia.

Coda

A - men! A - men! A - men! A - men! A - men! A - men!

87 BENEDICITE DOMINO

Bless the Lord, all you works of the Lord.

Canon

(A) *Calmly*   (B)

Be - ne - di - ci - te   om - ni - a   o - pe - ra   Do - mi - ni

(C)   (D)

Do - mi - no,   Do - mi - no.

88 BENEDICTUS

Blessed is he who comes in the name of the Lord.

Principal Canon

(A)   (B)

Be - ne - di - ctus qui ve - nit,   Be - ne - di - ctus qui ve - nit, in

(C)   (D)

no - mi - ne, in   no - mi - ne,   in no - mi - ne   Do - mi - ni.

CANTATE DOMINO

(Four canons on the same harmonic pattern using the same accompaniments)

1. Cantate Domino

Sing to the Lord, rejoice in God.

Can - ta - te Do - mi -no. Al - le - lu - ia, al - le -

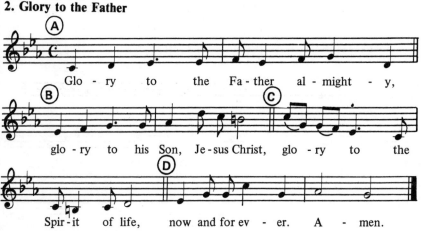

lu - ia! Ju - bi - la - te De - o.

2. Glory to the Father

Glo - ry to the Fa - ther al - might - y,

glo - ry to his Son, Je - sus Christ, glo - ry to the

Spir - it of life, now and for ev - er. A - men.

3. Gloria II (for Christmas)

Glory to God in the highest, and peace to his people on earth.

Rhythmically

Glo - ri - a, Glo - ri - a, in ex - cel - sis De - o,

Glo - ri - a, Glo - ri - a, al - le - lu - ia! Et in ter-ra pax ho -

mi - ni - bus bo - nae vo - lun - ta - tis.

4. Veni Creator Spiritus (for Pentecost)
Come, Holy Spirit

Ve - ni Cre - a - tor, Ve - ni Cre - a - tor,

Ve - ni Cre - a - tor Spi - ri - tus.

91 CHRISTUS VINCIT — JUBILATE COELI
Christ conquers, Christ reigns, Christ rules.
Heaven and earth rejoice for Jesus Christ is truly risen.

Double Canon (2nd canon ad lib.)

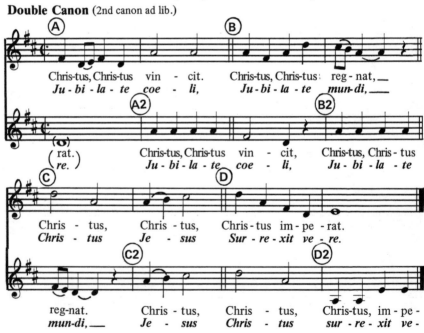

Chris-tus, Chris-tus vin - cit. Chris-tus, Chris-tus reg - nat,__
Ju - bi - la - te coe - li, Ju - bi - la - te mun-di,__

(rat.) Chris-tus, Chris-tus vin - cit, Chris-tus, Chris - tus
re.) Ju - bi - la - te coe - li, Ju - bi - la - te

Chris - tus, Chris - tus, Chris - tus im - pe - rat.
Chris - tus Je - sus Sur - re - xit ve - re.

reg-nat. Chris - tus, Chris - tus, Chris-tus, im - pe -
mun-di,__ Je - sus Chris - tus sur - re - xit ve -

24

CREDO II

We believe in one God, one Lord and one Spirit.

Ostinato Response (in Canon)

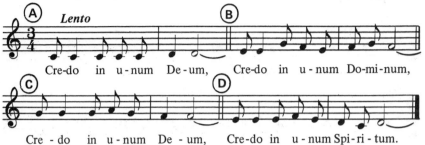

Cre-do in u-num De-um, Credo in u-num Do-mi-num,

Cre-do in u-num De-um, Cre-do in u-num Spi-ri-tum.

DA PACEM DOMINE

94

Give peace, O Lord.

Ostinato

Da pa-cem Do-mi-ne, Da

FOR YOURS IS THE KINGDOM

96

Canon

For yours is the King-dom, for yours is the power,

for yours is the King-dom, for yours is the power,

for yours is the glo-ry, for ev-er, A-men!

for yours is the glo-ry, for ev-er, A-men!

97

GLORIA IIı

Glory to God in the highest. Alleluia!
Christ is born today, the Savior has appeared.

Principal Canon

Glo - ri -a, glo - ri - a, in ex -cel -sis De - o!

Glo - ri -a, glo - ri - a, al - le - lu - ia, al - le - lu - ia!

99

HOSANNA

Hosanna in the highest.

Canon

Ho - san - na, ho - san - na, ho - san - na in ex -cel - sis. Ho -

100

JUBILATE DEO

Rejoice in God.

Canon (Praetorius)

Ju - bi - la - te De -o, Ju-bi-la - te De - o, A - le-lu - ia.

JUBILATE, SERVITE

Rejoice in God all the earth. Serve the Lord with gladness.

Canon

Ju - bi - la - te De - o om - nis ter - ra.

Ser - vi - te Do - mi - no in lae - ti - ti - a.

Al - le - lu - ia, al - le - lu - ia, in lae - ti - ti - a.

Al - le - lu - ia, al - le - lu - ia, in lae - ti - ti - a!

LAUDAMUS TE

We praise you, Lord.

103

Canon

Lau - da - mus te Do - mi - ne, lau - da - mus te Do - mi -

ne, lau - da - mus te Do - mi - ne.

104

MAGNIFICAT

My soul magnifies the Lord.

Principal Canon

Ma - gni - fi - cat, Ma - gni - fi - cat, Ma-gni-fi-cat a-ni-ma me-a Do-mi-num.

Ma - gni - fi - cat, Ma - gni - fi - cat, Ma-gni-fi-cat a-ni-ma me - a!

105

OSTENDE NOBIS

Lord, show us your mercy. Amen! Come soon!

Principal Canon

Lento

Os - ten - de no - bis Do - mi - ne, mi - se - ri -

cor - di - am tu - am. A - men! A - men! Ma - ra - na -

1.2.3. *(Fine)*

tha! Ma - ra - na - tha! Os - ten - de. - tha.

107

PATER SANCTE

Holy Father, listen to our pleading.

Canon

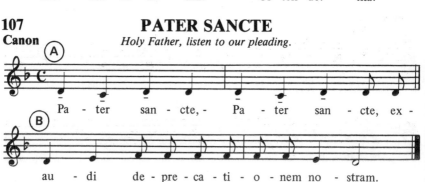

Pa - ter san - cte, - Pa - ter san - cte, ex -

au - di de - pre - ca - ti - o - nem no - stram.

PER CRUCEM

By your cross and passion, and by your holy resurrection, deliver us, O Lord.

Canon

Per cru - cem et pas - si - o - nem tu - am

Li - be - ra nos Do - mi - ne, li - be - ra nos Do - mi - ne,

li - be - ra nos Do - mi - ne, Do - mi - ne.

Per cru - cem et pas - si - o - nem tu - am.

Li - be - ra nos Do - mi - ne, li - be - ra nos Do - mi - ne,

li - be - ra nos Do - mi - ne, Do - mi - ne.

Per sanc - tam re - sur - rec - ti - o - nem tu - am.

Li - be - ra nos Do - mi - ne, li - be - ra nos Do - mi - ne,

li - be - ra nos Do - mi - ne, Do - mi - ne.

110 SALVATOR MUNDI

Principal Canon *Savior of the world, save us, free us.*

Sal - va-tor mun-di sal - va nos. Sal - va - tor mun-di sal - va nos.

Sal - va nos, sal - va nos. Sal - va-tor mun-di sal - va nos.

112 SANCTUS

Canon *Holy Lord, God of hosts.*

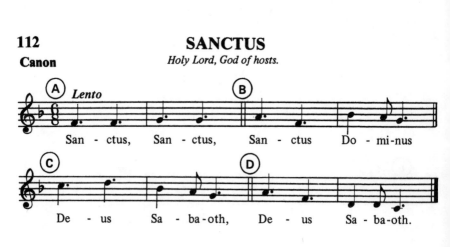

San - ctus, San - ctus, San - ctus Do - mi-nus

De - us Sa - ba-oth, De - us Sa - ba-oth.

SURREXIT DOMINUS VERE II

114

The Lord is truly risen! Christ is risen today!

Canon

TIBI DEO

115

*To you, God the Father, through the Son and in the Holy Spirit,
be all honor and glory for ever and ever. Amen.*

Canon

INDEX